POSITION JAZZ

10 up-beat original pieces for cello duet

by
PAT LEGG

FABER *ff* MUSIC

Preface

Position Jazz is a collection of ten cello duets designed to offer an enjoyable introduction to positions from ½ to 5th. The deliberately simple lower part enables the teacher, playing from memory, to observe the student above. It also provides an opportunity for a beginner cellist to experience making music with a more advanced pupil. Once the technique and style for each piece is secure, the student should be encouraged to improvise over the existing harmonic bass and rhythmic patterns. The positions used within each piece are indicated in boxes.

Pat Legg

© 1990 by Faber Music Ltd
First published in 1990 by Faber Music Ltd
3 Queen Square, London WC1N 3AU
Cover design by M & S Tucker
Music engraved by Sambo Music Engraving Co
Printed in England

Contents

1. HABANERA

2. WALTZ

3. RAGTIME

* 𝅗𝅥 last time.

4. BLUES

5. RHYTHM RAG

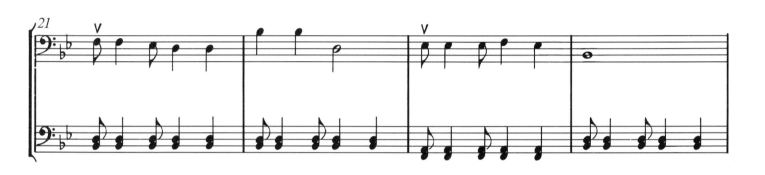

D.C. al ✛
poi al Coda

CODA rall.

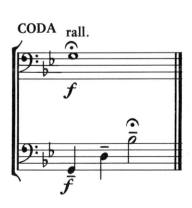

8

6. CABARET

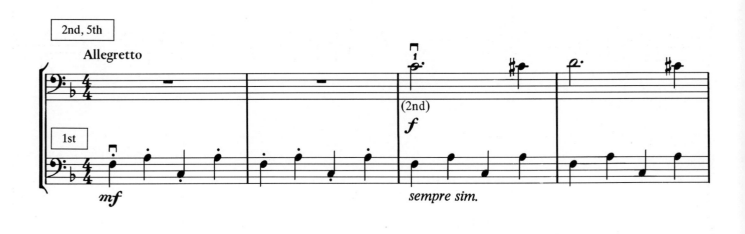

7. CARNIVAL RAG

8. LULLABY BLUES

9. MICRO WALTZ

10. RAGTIME DOLL